# A HANDFUL OF HAIKU

Mrs. R. Lipschutz

EDITOR   Marjorie L. Burns

DESIGNER   Marijka Kostiw

ART ACKNOWLEDGMENTS

Prints by Hokusai on pages 3, 11, 31, 33, 40, 43, 44, 51, and 52 are from the Picture Collection of the New York Public Library.

The remaining paintings (including the one on the cover), by unidentified Japanese artists, were kindly lent by Kathy Massaro.

ISBN 0-590-35581-3

12 11 10 9 8 7 6 5 4 3 2 1          8          9/8 0 1 2 3/9

# CONTENTS

# INTRODUCTION

There is something appealing about a miniature, whether that miniature is a horse, a painting, a baby's hand, or a three-line poem called a haiku. A miniature invites close inspection, and usually the more we look, the more we see in it. We marvel at the tiny creation, but not just because it is tiny: what impresses us most is that, in spite of its small size, it is a complete and well-made specimen of its kind.

A haiku is a complete and well-made poem in three short lines. This shortest of all verse forms was invented in Japan, where it has been extremely popular for six centuries with poets and non-poets alike. Today it seems that almost everyone in Japan, regardless of age or occupation, not only reads haiku but writes them. In recent decades haiku have also become popular in the English-speaking world, especially in the United States.

A traditional Japanese haiku obeys two basic rules. The first rule states that a haiku must contain exactly seventeen syllables arranged in three lines: five syllables in the first line, seven in the second, and five in the third. Some English translators or writers of haiku follow this rule. Others ignore it, arguing that rhythm in English verse depends on the number and arrangement of stresses (beats) in a line, not on the number of syllables. The haiku in this book represent a compromise: they all have three lines, but few of those lines have the required number of syllables.

The second basic rule states that every haiku must contain a reference to the season of the year. Sometimes the name of the season — spring, summer, autumn, or winter — is mentioned. More often, however, the season is indicated by some object that is asssociated with it. For example, plum blossoms, butterflies, and haze are signs of spring; an evening breeze indicates summer; crows and chrysanthemums mean autumn; and Mandarin ducks are associated with winter.

The reference to the season sets the scene, and the scene provides a context for the images in the poem. This is important because a haiku expresses its meaning primarily through images. The poet tries to choose images that are rich in associations, so that they will awaken memories and start trains of thought in readers' minds. The object is not to state the meaning but to suggest it in a way that helps readers discover it for themselves.

It is considered bad form for a poet or translator to come right out and tell the reader what an image means. The editor and translator Asataro Miyamori gives an interesting example of this kind of offense against the spirit of haiku:

> Lo! a crow sits on a bare bough;
> 'Tis a dreary autumn evening.

This translation of a famous haiku by Basho appears in the first edition of Miyamori's Anthology of Haiku Ancient and Modern. But in a later edition of the same book, Miyamori finds fault with it. He says the translation is clumsy because it contains the adjective "dreary," which is unnecessary. The alert reader, he says, will realize that the scene is dreary without being told. In fact, every detail of the image has melancholy or unpleasant associations: (1) The crow is an awkward, raucous-voiced bird that feeds on carrion, or dead flesh. (2) The leafless branch of a tree suggests death. (3) Autumn is the season when nature appears to be dying. (4) Evening brings the fading of the light.

Miyamori believes that the following translation is truer to Basho's original, which is considered by many critics to be an ideal haiku:

> A crow is perched on a bare branch;
> It is an autumn eve.

Miyamori defines an ideal haiku as "one in which a natural event is described as it is, and the poet's emotion does not appear on the surface." In other words, an ideal haiku is one that gives you, the reader, a chance to play an important role. For, as you call up from your own imagination the thoughts and feelings suggested by the images, you become a participant in the making of a poem.

# THE OLD POND

An old, neglected pond:
Splash! the sound
of a frog jumping in!

**BASHO**

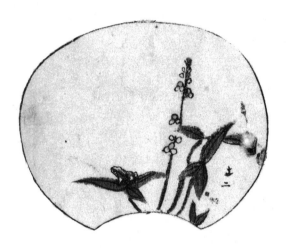

Near Basho's small house there was an unused fishpond. As he was sitting quietly one afternoon (the mention of a frog tells us it was a spring afternoon), he heard a splashing sound and immediately composed the last two lines of this haiku. Later he added the first line to complete the poem. "The Old Pond," which is Basho's most famous poem, is typical of the new style of haiku that he originated. It is regarded by many as a model of the ideal haiku.

## MY ROAD

Along this road
no one goes but me
as autumn twilight falls.

*BASHO*

*The poet wrote this haiku in September 1694 at a tea house in the suburbs of Osaka. The road that ran in front of the tea house — the road that Basho was traveling — was deserted. Not another soul was in sight. According to one critic, the lonely road represents Basho's life as a man of literature. Although he had many pupils, he was afraid that none of them would be able to keep the Basho Style alive after he was gone.*

# NEW YEAR'S DAY

The first day of the year:
I think of loneliness
and an autumn dusk.

**BASHO**

*Basho's thoughts are not the kind that a person is supposed to have
on New Year's Day.*

## TAKEN ILL WHILE TRAVELING

Illness ends my journey,
but over withered fields
my dreams still wander.

**BASHO**

The mention of withered fields shows that the season is winter.
Basho died in 1694 while on a journey with some of his friends and
pupils. As he lay in what was clearly his last illness, his companions
asked him to give them a "death poem" — a verse that would
summarize his philosophy of life. He refused, saying that every poem
he had written since "The Old Pond" was a death poem. But that
night he had a dream, which, on waking, he made into this farewell.

## ENJOYING THE EVENING COOL

With a companion
who doesn't speak all he thinks,
I enjoy the cool of the evening.

*HYAKUCHI*

*The cool of the evening is something that people enjoy in the summer.*

## ALONE

A flitting firefly!
I want to cry, "Look!"
But ah! I am alone.

*TAIGI*

Fireflies are associated with summer, when swarms of them may be seen hovering over bodies of water. A popular pastime in Japan is to go to the banks of a river on a fine summer night and watch the thousands of tiny lights sparkling in the darkness. Of course, in this poem there is only a single firefly that has somehow gotten into the poet's room.

## THE COW I SOLD

The cow I sold
is leaving the village
through the haze.

*HYAKUCHI*

*Haze is associated with spring.*

## THE MORNING-GLORY

Because a morning-glory
has captured my well-bucket,
I beg water from a neighbor.

*CHIYO-NI*

*The poet cannot lower her bucket into the well without harming the morning-glory vine that has twined itself around the rope. The morning-glory is a summer flower.*

## BATH WATER

I have nowhere to throw
the bath water:
insects singing sweetly all around.

**ONITSURA**

*To the Japanese, the sounds made by insects are not noisy chirps but lovely songs.*

# THE BRIGHT MOON

How brightly shone the moon!
Only the insects' songs
gave proof that it was night.

### ETSUJIN

*Both the bright moon and the singing insects are indicators of
autumn.*

## ORPHAN SPARROW

Come here to me
and let's play together,
little motherless sparrow.

*ISSA*

*Issa is said to have composed this poem when he was nine years old. His mother had died when he was three, and his father had remarried. The stepmother neglected Issa in favor of her own son, so that the boy felt like an orphan. According to the story, it was a holiday in the village and all the children had new clothes except Issa. He looked so shabby that the other children refused to play with him. Seeing a forlorn baby sparrow that had apparently fallen from the nest, Issa spoke these lines and then burst into tears.*

## THE GALAXY

The beautiful River of Heaven
shows through the holes
in my paper door.

*ISSA*

*Issa was so poor that he could not afford to repair the holes in his paper door. The River of Heaven is the Milky Way, and the season is the one in which the Milky Way is most clearly seen: autumn.*

## BIRDS' NESTS

Not knowing that the tree
will soon be cut down,
the birds are building their nests in it.

*ISSA*

# A PROUD NOBLEMAN

What can make His Lordship the daimyo
get down off his horse?
Cherry blossoms!

*ISSA*

*In old Japan, a daimyo was a high-ranking nobleman. When a
daimyo rode along a highway, ordinary people were expected to get
off their horses and squat by the side of the road until he had
passed. The daimyo in this poem sees a cherry tree in bloom and
dismounts in order to get close to the flowers and admire them. His
action is not surprising: the Japanese as a people have always
revered nature, and they consider the cherry blossom to be one of
nature's greatest glories.*

## THE RED MOON

What a bright red moon!
Tell me, children,
who owns it?

*ISSA*

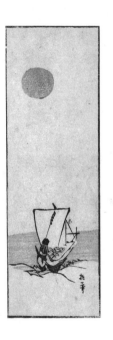

## WATCH OUT!

Out of the way, baby sparrow,
get out of the way!
The Honorable Mr. Horse is coming!

*ISSA*

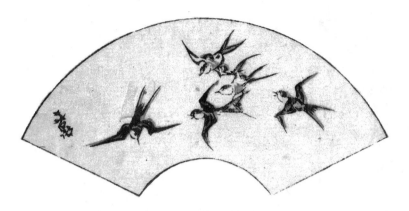

## THE GREAT BUDDHA'S NOSE

The huge statue of Buddha:
out of its nose
flies a swallow.

*ISSA*

*The poet may be referring to the Daibutsu (Great Buddha) at Kamakura, which is 49 feet, 7 inches high and has a nose 3 feet, 9 inches long. The swallow is associated with spring.*

## THE NIGHTINGALE'S SONG

The nightingale sings
the same song for everyone,
including His Lordship.

*ISSA*

*The nightingale is an indicator of spring.*

## THE KITE

Over their hovel
the beggar's children
are flying a beautiful kite.

*ISSA*

## A CAGED BIRD

See, with what envious eyes
the caged bird gazes
at the butterflies!

*ISSA*

## POISONOUS MUSHROOMS

It can kill you,
this kind of mushroom,
though it does look pretty.

*ISSA*

## VIOLETS

Dawn in the garden,
and the violets are aslant.
It was done by a mole.

*BONCHO*

*Violets are associated with spring.*

## A SCARECROW

What was that noise?
A scarecrow, all by itself,
has tumbled to the ground.

*BONCHO*

*Harold Henderson, an American authority on haiku, says that in the original Japanese this poem, "with its suggestion of unseen powers about us, is capable of making cold shivers run down one's spine."*

# SPRING RAIN

In soft spring rain
a paper umbrella and a straw raincoat
walk chatting together.

*BUSON*

## A BLUE HERON

An evening breeze blows,
and the water ripples
against the blue heron's legs.

*BUSON*

*The evening breeze indicates that the season is summer.*

## WIND AND LEAVES

O leaves, ask the wind
which of you will be the first
to fall off.

**SOSEKI**

## GIVEN TO MY PUPIL ENSUI

Yield to the willow
all passions, all desires
of your heart.

**BASHO**

*Because the willow tree is pliant and bows before the wind, it comes through the storm unbroken. The willow indicates that the season is spring.*

## THE MOON AND CLOUDS

Clouds veil the moon now and again,
giving its beholders
a chance to rest.

**BASHO**

*On nights when the moon is full, people like to go outdoors and look at it. This poem suggests that moon-gazing is not a passive recreation.*

## THE HARVEST MOON

The fields and hills,
look — they are as clear as day!
My neck aches from watching.

*ONITSURA*

*The harvest moon is the full moon of September 22-23, which is considered the brightest and loveliest full moon of the year.*

# MY SHADOW

Going home after viewing
the bright harvest moon,
my shadow leads the way.

### SODO

## THE MOON AND THE PINE

I hung the bright moon
on the pine tree, and then
I took it off again.

**HOKUSHI**

*The arrangement of the objects in the scene depends on where the viewer is standing.*

## *YOUNG FOLIAGE*

Trees with new green leaves
thickly cover the earth,
leaving only Mount Fuji unburied!

*BUSON*

At 12,388 feet, Mount Fuji is the highest mountain in Japan. There
are trees only at the foot of the mountain.

# THE PASSING OF SPRING

Every year when spring passes,
the sadness is the same,
but I am not the same.

### GEKKYO

## YEAR'S END

Another year is gone;
I have kept my gray hair hidden
from my parents.

**ETSUJIN**

# THE CHERRY BLOSSOMS AT UENO

In the shade of the blossoming
cherry trees, utter strangers
there are none!

*ISSA*

*Ueno is a park in Tokyo. When the cherry trees are in bloom, people stroll leisurely through the park, admiring the blossoms. They are in a holiday mood and exchange friendly greetings with everyone they meet.*

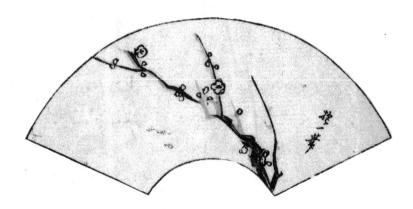

## CHERRY BLOSSOM TIME

Skeletons all dressed up
in their finest raiment —
it is flower-viewing time.

### ONITSURA

*Most critics have assumed that the "dressed-up skeletons" are the
people who have come to view the cherry blossoms and that Onitsura
is being slightly sarcastic about them. However, as Harold
Henderson points out, the description in the first two lines applies
equally well to the cherry trees. Perhaps the poet had both the
people and the trees in mind when he wrote this haiku.*

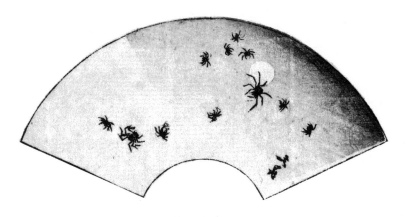

## MOON-VIEWING

In any garments
we appear beautiful
under the bright moon.

**CHIYO-NI**

## A SILVERY WORLD

All the fields and hills
have been captured by the snow
and nothing is left.

*JOSO*

# EARLY SPRING

On the plum tree
one warm bloom,
one blossom's worth of spring.

*RANSETSU*

*After the long, cold winter, the poet sees the first sign of spring warmth, a plum blossom. The Japanese rank the plum blossom second only to the cherry blossom in beauty.*

## SUN AND MOON

The sun and moon
are glaring at each other
in east and west.

**SHIKI**

## THE AYU

If they had voices,
ayu would cry at the sight
of the cormorant fishing boat.

*ETSUJIN*

*The ayu is a very tasty freshwater trout. Japanese fishermen train
cormorants — large, web-footed water birds with long bills — to
dive under the water and catch the ayu for them. A tight strap or
whalebone ring around each bird's neck prevents it from swallowing
the fish. The fisherman draws the cormorant back to the boat by
means of a cord and forces it to cough up the contents of its throat.*

## THE WINTER MOON

The icy moon
paints the shadows of trees
on the snow.

*KUBUTSU*

## THE MAPLE LEAVES

How I envy maple leaves
that turn so red and beautiful
and then fall!

**SHIKO**

*Maple leaves fall while they are still at the height of their glory.*

## A SUMMER SHOWER

The summer shower has passed,
leaving the brilliant moon
upon the grass.

*SHO-U*

## WHITE HERONS

But for their cries,
the herons would be lost to sight
in the snow of this morn.

*CHIYO-NI*

## THE PUNY FROG

Puny frog, keep fighting,
don't let yourself be beaten!
Issa is here to cheer you on!

*ISSA*

*The poet wrote this haiku after attending a frog fight. As usual, he took the side of the "underdog."*

## THE FLY

Oh, don't swat that fly!
He's wringing his hands!
He's wringing his feet!

**ISSA**

## THE NIGHTINGALE

The nightingale,
when it stops singing,
is only a green bird.

*ONITSURA*

*The nightingale is associated with springtime.*

## A CROW ON A SNOWY MORNING

The usually hateful crow —
even he is lovely
on this morn of snow.

*BASHO*

## A FALLEN FLOWER

A fallen petal flies back
to the branch it fell from.
Oh! It's a butterfly!

**MORITAKE**